Weight Watcher

Freestyle

Cookbook 2018

Discover how to lose weight fast with this Ultimate, All New Weight watchers Freestyle Recipes!

Daniel Fisher

Copyright page

ISBN-13: 978-1-948191-20-3

ISBN-10: 1-948191-20-2

Printed in The U.S.A

Table of Contents

I want to personally Congratulate you and thank you for Purchasing my book " Weight Watchers Freestyle Cookbook 2018: *Discover how to lose weight fast with this Ultimate, All New Weight watchers Freestyle Recipes!"*

This is the only book you'll need to lose those stubborn fats this year. You'll Discover the New Weight watchers plan everyone is talking about, Freestyle and Flex. Also, there are New, tasty and healthy Recipes that are easy to make and will help you achieve your weight loss goal. We also included a Smart Weekly Planner to help you plan your meals every week. The Freestyle and Flex Plan will Jumpstart your New Weight loss goal and we believe in no time, you'll lose those Fat rapidly. Now let's get Started!

Introduction

Weight watchers is a diet plan aimed at those who are looking to lose weight, without eliminating certain food groups. Weight watchers have a point value for every food, and those points are known as Weight watchers Smartpoints.

Weight watchers Freestyle Plan

According to the Weight Watcher Site, these new addition provide a foundation in which members can build a healthy pattern of eating. The foods were selected because they provide high quality nutrition and also form the basis of a healthy diet without posing a risk of over indulgence, thereby making it easier for one to pay attention to when satisfied as opposed to overeating.

Weight watchers freestyle plan is based on SmartPoints System, which encourages the consumption of fruits, vegetables, lean proteins and less sugars. This new program was launched in the last month of 2017.

It is an expansion of Smartpoint and 'Behind the scale' which was released three years ago. Under the old plan, every food had a smart point value- with majority of the vegetables having smart point values. The new plan is an expansion of the food points list to include lean proteins. The Smartpoints budget is customized for each member based on their age, weight, height, and gender. All information would be gotten during sign up into weight watchers, and then personal daily points tailored for each person.

Even though it seems like a mix between Smartpoint and simply filling (weight watchers no point option), there are some noticeable differences between both plans. In Freestyle:

- Daily smart points budgets are given, so also are weekly smart point for excess.

- There is a zero point food list, which includes eggs, corn, boneless chicken breast, vegetables, lentils, tofu, and sea food. Roll over points- Up to four Smartpoints roll over, into weeklies, on the condition that one tracks an item a day which has to be less than four.

- Less tracking, the added food values doesn't need to be weighed or tracked. Hence the flexibility of the new weight program.

- Due to the expanded zero smart points food list, daily smart points are adjusted- reduced, to balance out the zero points food addition and account for the extra calories that may accumulate as a result of the unlimited foods.

- There are over two hundred newly added zero smart points items.

- It has a 14 point range.

Whereas in Simply filling:

- The Smartpoints budget is weekly Smartpoints only.

- Simply filling allows a broader list free foods (foods one is allowed to select on their own); the freestyle zero smartpoints foods, whole grains, cheese, reduced-calorie bread, red meat, healthy oil etc.

- Simply filling doesn't permit roll overs.

The goal of the weight watchers freestyle plan is to give people the free rein to eat whatever they enjoy, bearing in mind that one is less likely to stray from the diet that they enjoy. It has also been shown that people have a certain reserve toward weight loss plans that restrict certain food classes.

The Freestyle plan uses the Smartpoint. The Smartpoints is a counting system adopted from the Propoints system. It encourages members to make healthier, nutritious choices by eating less sugar and saturated fat and simply counting calories. With foods higher in sugar or saturated fats having higher Smartpoints values, and foods higher in lean proteins, lower Smartpoints values, members are nudged toward healthier eating choices.

- Here, every food is assigned its own Smartpoint values based on its composition of calories, protein, saturated fat and sugar.
- Foods rich in protein have lower Smartpoints value.
- Saturated fat and Sugar increases Smartpoints value.

- Smartpoints are easy to track as they are calculated in whole numbers, and can be tracked with some tools.

The Freestyle Smartpoint system uses the latest nutritional and weight loss science to make healthy eating as flexible (one is not constricted by dieting) and easy as possible. Every food and drink have a Smartpoints value, a number that is based on calories, protein, sugar and saturated fat. The baseline Smartpoints value is based on the food's calories. Protein lowers the Smartpoints value, while saturated fat and sugar increases the Smartpoints value.

Each day, a Smartpoint budget is given, to be used on any food item as desired. Daily smartpoints budget is calculated based on age, height, weight, and gender, with 23 being the minimum daily value. Only the foods with smart point values need to be track. One, is only expected to track the foods with Smartpoints value. All zero smartpoints foods aren't required to be tracked.

Each week, a weekly smartpoint budget (weeklies) is given- this is given in the instance one's daily smartpoints budgets have been exceeded. This way you can be able to lose weight easily.

The New Weight watchers plan is making losing weight very easy, they have included lots of yummy foods you'll enjoy; this include plant based protein sources like turkey, eggs, tofu, chicken, lentils, yogurt and beans with lean animal inclusive. In addition, you'll get to enjoy your favorite sweetcorn and peas freely on the new plans.

200 New Zero Point Food List:

Apple

Applesauce

Apricots

Arrowroot

Artichoke hearts

Artichokes

Arugula

Asparagus

Bamboo shoots

Banana

Beans

Beets

Berries

Blackberries

Blueberries

Broccoli

Broccoli rabe

Broccoli slaw'

Broccolini

Brussels sprouts

Cabbage

Calamari

Cantaloupe

Carrots

Cauliflower

Caviar

Celery

Swiss chard

Chicken breast(fat free)

Chicken breast or tenderloin

Clementines

Coleslaw mix

Collards

Corn

Cranberries

Cucumber

Daikon

Dates

Dragon fruit

Edamame

Egg substitutes

Egg whites

Eggplant

Eggs (whole)

Endive

Escarole

Fennel

Figs

Fish

Fish fillet

Fruit cocktail

Fruit cup

Fruit salad

Fruit

Garlic

Ginger root

Grape fruit

Grapes

Greens

Greens, mixed baby

Guavas

Guava, Strawberry

Hearts of palm

Honey dew melon

Jack fruit

Jerk Chicken Breast

Jerusalem artichokes

Jicama

Kiwifruit

Kohlrabi

Kumquats

Leeks

Lemon

Lemon zest

Lentils

Lettuce

Lime

Lime zest

Litchis

Mangoes

Melon balls

Mung bean sprouts

Mung dal

Mushroom caps

Mushrooms

Nectarine

Nori seaweed

Okra

Onions

Oranges

Papayas

Parseley

Passion fruit

Pea shoots

Peaches

Peapods, black-eye

Pears

Peas and carrots

Peas

Peppers

Pepperoncini

Persimmons

Pickles

Pico de gallo

Pimientos

Pine apple

Plumcots

Plums

Pomegranates

Pomelo

Pumpkin

Pumpkin puree

Radicchio

Radishes

Raspberries

Rutabagas

Salad, mixed greens

Salad, side (no dressing)

Salad, three-bean

Sala, tossed(no dressing)

Salsa verde

Salsa, fat free

Salsa, fat free, glutton free

Sashimi

Satay, chicken

Satsuma mandarin

Sauerkraut

Scallions

Seaweed

Shallots

Shellfish

Spinach

Sprouts

Squash, summer

Squash winter

Starfruit

Strawberries

Succotash

Tangelo

Tangerine

Taro

Tofu

Tofu, smoked

Tomatillos

Tomato puree

Tomato sauce

Tomatoes

Turkey breast (ground)

Turkey breast or tenderloin

Turkey breast(skinless)

Turnips

Vegetable sticks

Vegetables, mixed

Vegetables, stir fry

Water chestnuts

Watercress

Watermelon

Yoghurt (Greek)

Yoghurt (plain)

Yoghurt, soy

How to Use the Activity Points

Activity Points are also known as FitPoints, and can be earned through exercising. This points can be swapped for smart points, thereby increasing the food points one is allowed to eat in a day.

Fitpoints, just like smartpoints are assigned to members upon registration, and the point assigned to the member is based on their weight, age, gender, and activity level. Each member is given a Fitpoints goal for the week, and that increases based on his/her performance in meeting up to those weekly goals. This, the weight watchers do to encourage activity so weight loss is not through dieting alone.

The activity could range from, walking, jogging, running or dancing- as every movement count. The higher the intensity of the activity being performed, the higher the heart rate. The activities intensity (Exercise Intensity Levels) are divided into three as measured by the heart rate.

- High Intensity – Breathing here is labored, and one can only speak in short phrases.

- Moderate intensity- with a heart rate of 93 to 118 beats per minute, breathing is noticeably deeper. One can carry out conversations, but only intermittently.

- Low intensity- There is no noticeable change in the breathing patter, and this activities does not induce sweating.

Any activity done at the following levels are necessary for weight loss. Although the higher the intensity of the activity and the longer time spent doing the exercise, the greater energy expended which implies the greater weight lost.

Activity Points values are calculated using the level of intensity, body weight and time spent exercising to calculate the amount of energy expended.

How to calculate weight watchers activity points and Smart Points.

Weight Watcher Points Calculator is set to calculate the values based on age, gender, height, weight, and activity level of the member. Specific points are added based on those aspects.

Gender

Male= +8

Female =+2

Age

17 – 26years = + 4 points

27- 37years = + 2 points

38 – 47years = +2 points

48- 58years = +1

Weight

Per ten pounds of body weight = +1

Height

5.1ft − 5.10ft = +1 point

> 5.10ft = +2 points

Activity level

High activity= +6 points

Moderate activity = +2 points

Low activity = +0 points

Addition of the above factors gives one the amount of Smartpoints that they are allowed to eat in a day. The points should be recalculated every two to four weeks to account for the weight loss.

To study the amount of points in each food, study the nutritional information of the processed product and divide the total calories and grams of fat by 50 and twelve respectively. Add the numbers together - the nutritional break down of none packaged foods and vegetables can be obtained from online websites or by contacting a nutritionist. Next, divide the total amount of dietary fiber by 5 and subtract from the number gotten by adding the result of the calorie and gram division. Deduct each meal from the total amount of daily points.

An easier method of calculating the points, is by using weight watchers brand meals or recipes.

Secrets of losing weight with the Zero Point Diet

There are two approaches to losing weight on weight watchers

1. Count Smartpoint approach – this allows one to eat whichever food, using the daily and weekly budgets- giving one the freedom and flexibility of eating whatever they want.

2. No Count Approach/ Freestyle- this allows one a selected list of healthy foods, which should be strictly followed. However, one isn't expected to count or track them – and a weekly allowance for foods not included on the list is given.

In theory, it is believed that about 3500 calories is equivalent to one pound of body weight, and using this as a basis- to lose a pound each week, one must reduce their intake by about 500 calories a day, and by making those changes in one's diet, one can lose an a average of two pounds in a week.

Although this value is not uniform in the subsequent weeks on weight watchers- some weeks one might lose more or less than two pounds, one, however can be certain they're on the right tract if one averages the loss of two pounds at the end of the month (4*2/ 2). The weight lost during the first month is usually rapid due to the body's adjustment to the healthier consumption of food. The weight however been lost is known as the water weight, the body fat requires a longer time to be burned off and hence the need for earning fitpoints.

We have included in this section some wonderful Zero Point Food Ideas You can Start making now that will help you attain maximum weight loss. They are easy to Make you should Try Them.

- Pumpkin pancakes made with half cup canned pumpkin, Two whisked eggs, and a dash of cinnamon.

- Banana pancakes made with one mashed banana, 2 whisked eggs, and a dash of cinnamon.

- Two eggs scrambled with half cup black beans and salsa with a side of fruit.

- Two poached eggs with leftover roasted veggies and 1/2 cup lentils.

- One cup nonfat Greek yogurt with fresh fruit and cinnamon

- Lettuce tacos with taco seasoning and cooked ground turkey, half cup pinto beans, veggies, and salsa

- Green salad with turkey breast or cooked chicken

- Canned tuna mixed with nonfat Greek yogurt, mustard, and diced celery in lettuce wraps or a hollowed out tomato

- Leftover cooked fish with lentils and veggies

- Egg salad made with nonfat Greek yogurt, mustard, and diced celery in lettuce wraps or salad.

- Crust less quiche made with veggies, eggs and served with green salad

- Stir-fry with lean chicken or turkey (or tofu), lots of veggies, and soy sauce served with cauliflower rice

- Ground chicken or turkey burgers served in lettuce wraps with bake carrot fries

- Baked salmon with vegetables and chickpeas

- Roasted chicken with lentils and roasted vegetables.

Zero Point Snack and Dessert Ideas

- Microwave egg mugs

- fruit with Nonfat Greek yogurt

- Banana n'ice cream

- Banana pancakes made with one mashed banana, Two whisked eggs, and a dash of cinnamon for dessert

Delicious & Healthy WW Freestyle Recipes

We have made for you lot's of delicious and healthy WW Freestyle Recipes you can start using now.

Most of the recipes contains more of the zero points food, We have limited those foods the will be harmful to your health e.g. Sugar, Grains, labelled Diet Food, Processed Food, Alcohol and deep fried food.

We incorporated most of the healthy foods e.g. Egg, meat, seafoods, fruits, vegetables, nuts and seeds.

We hope you enjoy this meal as much as we do.

Ingredients
20 pecan halves, toasted
4-6 ounces semisweet chocolate morsels

How you make it:

1. In a microwave-safe bowl, microwave the chocolate morsels on high for about 1-1 1/2 minutes (or until melted), stirring every 30 seconds.
2. Dip half of each pecan half in melted chocolate, then place on a wax paper-lined baking sheet.
3. Let cool completely.
4. Store in an airtight container for up to 2 days.

Servings: 20 pecans

Nutritional information for one serving:

Freestyle SmartPoints: 1
Calories: 41
Calories from fat: 24
Total fat: 2.8g
Cholesterol: 0mg
Total carbs: 4g
Fiber: 0.6g
Protein: 0.4g

Ingredients

1/2 peach (use canned peach halves in light syrup)

1/3-1/2 cup vanilla yogurt

How you make it

1. Using the back of a spoon, spread the vanilla yogurt into a circle on a plate.

2. Place the peach half, flat side down, in the center of the yogurt.

3. Repeat these steps for each additional serving if desired.

Servings: 1

Nutritional information for one serving:

Freestyle SmartPoints: 0

Calories: 68

Calories from fat: 24

Total fat: 2.8g

Cholesterol: 10mg Fiber: 0.7g

Protein: 3.3g Total carbs: 8.5g

Makes 8 servings
Ingredients

1 (15 ounce) can chickpeas, drained
1/4 cup orange juice
1/4 cup fresh parsley leaves
2 tablespoons tahini (sesame seed paste)
1 garlic clove
2 tablespoons chopped onions
2 tablespoons rice vinegar
1 teaspoon Dijon mustard
1 teaspoon low sodium soy sauce
1/4 teaspoon ground cumin
1/4 teaspoon ground coriander
1/4 teaspoon ground turmeric
1/4 teaspoon paprika
1/4 teaspoon ground ginger
1/4 teaspoon salt

How you Make it:

1. Place the orange juice, garlic, onion and parsley in a blender or food processor and process until smooth.

2. Add all the remaining ingredients and process until smooth.

3. Serve with raw vegetables or pita triangles.

Freestyle SMARTPOINTS per serving: 1

Nutritional information per serving: 92 calories, 2.5g fat, 2.9g fiber

Makes 4 servings

Ingredients
1 lb sweet potatoes, peeled
1 tablespoon extra-virgin olive oil
1 teaspoon cajun seasoning (or to taste)
salt (to taste)

How you make it:

1. Preheat the oven to 375 degrees F.
2. Quarter the potatoes and cut into 1/4 inch thick strips.
3. Spread the potatoes on a lightly oiled baking sheet, sprinkle with olive oil and Cajun seasoning and toss to coat.
4. Bake in the lower third of the oven for about 30 minutes, stirring occasionally.
5. Season with salt to taste and serve hot.
Freestyle Smartpoint per serving: 2
Nutritional information per serving: 127 calories, 3.4g fat, 3.4g fiber

Makes 4 servings

Ingredients
3/4 lb ground turkey
1/3 cup Monterey Jack cheese
2 scallions or green onions, chopped
1 tablespoon ketchup
1 tablespoon soy sauce
1/4 teaspoon garlic powder
1/4 teaspoon pepper

How you make it:

1. In a bowl, combine all the ingredients (except the cheese).
2. Blend in the cheese.
3. Form into 4 patties.
4. Spray a frying pan with cooking spray.
5. Cook the patties until done.
6. Serve on hamburger buns with lettuce and tomatoes.

Freestyle Smartpoint per serving: 4
Nutritional information per serving: 171 calories, 9.9g fat, 0.3g fiber

Makes 8 servings

Ingredients

4 (3-ounce) hoagie rolls, cut in half lengthwise

8 slices of smoked turkey

8 (3/4-ounce) slices low-fat Swiss cheese

8 sandwich-length pickle slices

cooking spray

For the garlic Dijon butter

1 whole head garlic

1 tablespoon Dijon mustard

1 teaspoon olive oil

1 1/2 teaspoons butter, softened

How you make it

1. Preheat the oven to 350° F.

2. To prepare the butter: remove the white papery skin from garlic head (do not peel or separate the cloves); drizzle with oil.

3. Wrap the garlic head in foil. Bake at 350° F for about 1 hour; let cool for 10 minutes.

4. Separate the garlic cloves; squeeze to extract the garlic pulp. Discard the skins.

5. In a small bowl, combine the garlic pulp, butter and Dijon mustard; set aside.

6. To prepare the sandwiches: scoop out the inside of the roll halves, leaving a 1/2-inch shell.

7. Spread about 2 teaspoons garlic butter over the cut sides of the top and bottom halves of each roll.

8. Arrange the turkey, pickles and cheese evenly on the bottom halves of the rolls; top with the top halves.

9. Heat a nonstick grill pan over medium-high heat. Coat the pan with cooking spray.

10. Add 2 sandwiches to the pan. Place a cast-iron or heavy skillet on top of the sandwiches, pressing gently to flatten.

11. Grill for about 4 minutes on each side (or until the cheese melts and the bread is toasted).

12. Repeat the procedure with the remaining 2 sandwiches.

13. Cut the sandwiches in half diagonally, and serve immediately.

One serving is 1/2 sandwich.

Freestyle Smart points per serving: 4

Nutritional information per serving: 187 calories, 10.5g fat, 0.7g fiber

Makes 4 servings

Ingredients
2 cups large cherry tomatoes
1 garlic clove
1/2-1 dried red chili, crumbled (or red pepper flakes)
2 teaspoons extra-virgin olive oil
4 slices country bread
sea salt
freshly ground black pepper

How you make it:

1. Heat the broiler or grill. Set the cooking rack 3 inches from the heat.
2. Place the tomatoes on a rimmed baking pan. Broil them for about 2 minutes (until they soften and the skins start to blister and split).
3. Using tongs, flip the tomatoes and broil them for about 2 more minutes (until blistered but not totally soft).
4. Transfer the tomatoes to a serving dish and lightly squash with a fork so some of the juices run out.
5. Sprinkle with olive oil, chili, salt and pepper; and gently fold to combine.

6. Serve over toasted country bread that has been rubbed with a garlic clove.

WW Freestyle Smartpoints per serving: 1
Nutritional information per serving: 171 calories, 5.3g fat, 4.3g fiber

Makes 2 servings

Ingredients
2 bananas
2 tablespoons honey (or to taste)
granola cereal (optional)

How you make it:

1. Slice the bananas into two small bowls.
2. Drizzle honey over top; sprinkle with granola if desired.

Freestyle SmartPoints per serving: 1
Nutritional information per serving: 168 calories, 0.4g fat, 3.1g fiber

Makes 4 servings

Ingredients
1 (1/3 ounce) package sugar-free orange gelatin
1 (1 ounce) package sugar-free instant vanilla pudding mix
1 3/4 cups cold milk
1/4 cup boiling water
1/2 teaspoon vanilla extract

How you make it:

1. Combine the gelatin and the boiling water. Stir until dissolved.
2. Combine the cold milk and pudding mix.
3. Beat for 2 minutes with an electric mixer.
4. Add the gelatin mixture and vanilla extract. Mix well.
5. Pour into serving dishes or moulds. Chill until firm.
One serving is approximately 130 grams.

Freestyle Smartpoints per serving: 1
Nutritional information per serving: 97 calories, 4g fat, 0.1g fiber

Makes 24 popovers

Ingredients
3 ounces Roquefort cheese, crumbled
1 cup all-purpose flour
2 eggs, at room temperature
1 1/4 cups milk, at room temperature
1 tablespoon unsalted butter, melted
1 tablespoon finely chopped fresh flat-leaf parsley
1/2 teaspoon salt
1/4 teaspoon freshly ground white pepper

How you make it:

1. Position a rack in the lower third of an oven and preheat to 450 degrees F.
2. Generously brush two 12-cup mini-muffin pans with vegetable oil.
3. In a large bowl, whisk together the flour, parsley, salt and white pepper.
4. In a large measuring cup, whisk together the eggs, milk and butter.
5. Pour the wet ingredients over the dry ingredients and whisk together until just combined.
6. Pour the batter into the prepared muffin cups to within

about 1/4 inch of the rim (about 1 ½ tablespoons each).

7. Place a scant 1 teaspoon crumbled Roquefort cheese in the center of each filled cup.

8. Bake for about 10 minutes (do not open the oven door during this time!).

9. Reduce the oven temperature to 350 degrees F and continue to bake for about 8-10 more minutes (until the popovers are brown and crusty and fully puffed).

10. Remove the popovers from the oven and immediately transfer them to a napkin-lined bowl or warmed platter.

11. Serve immediately, or let cool on wire racks for up to 2 hours, then reheat in a 350 degrees F oven for about 10 minutes.

WW Freestyle Smartpoints per serving: 0

Nutritional information per serving: 50 calories, 2.5g fat, 0.2g fiber

Makes 12 servings

Ingredients
1 lb boneless skinless chicken breasts
1 cup crushed corn flakes
1 tablespoon finely snipped parsley
1/3 cup bottled Blue Cheese salad dressing
1-2 teaspoon bottled Tabasco sauce
celery ribs
1/4 teaspoon salt
2 teaspoons water

How you make it:
1. In a shallow bowl or pie plate, combine the crushed corn flakes, parsley and salt.
2. Cut the chicken breasts into strips about 3/4 inch wide and 3 inches long.
3. In a large mixing bowl, combine the 1/3 cup Blue Cheese dressing, Tabasco sauce and water.
4. Add the chicken, stir well to coat.
5. Roll the chicken pieces individually in the crumb mixture to coat.
6. Place the strips on a foil lined baking sheet.

7. Freeze for about 2 hours (until firm).

8. Place the frozen strips in a freezer container.

9. Cover and freeze up to 1 month.

10. To serve, heat the oven to 425 degrees F.

11. Place the frozen chicken strips in a single layer in a lightly greased 15x10x1 baking pan.

12. Bake for about 18-20 minutes (until the meat is no longer pink in center and the crumbs turn golden).

13. Serve warm with celery sticks and additional Blue Cheese dressing for dipping.

Freestyle Smartpoints per serving: 1

Nutritional information per serving: 84 calories, 4g fat, 0.1g fiber

Makes 20 small cakes

Ingredients
500 g salmon fillets, skin removed
3 tablespoons fine cornflour
1 egg white
1 tablespoon finely chopped ginger
3 kaffir lime leaves, shredded
3 tablespoons chopped flat leaf parsley
1 teaspoon wasabi
For the lime dipping sauce
1/4 cup lime juice
1/4 cup soy sauce
2 tablespoons brown sugar

How you make it:

1. To make the salmon cakes, remove any bones from the salmon and chop into 1/4 inch (5mm) dices.
2. Combine the chopped salmon with the egg white, corn flour, lime leaves, ginger, chopped parsley and wasabi paste; mix well.
3. Grill the cakes (or fry them in oil) on each side, until they turn golden brown. Drain the cakes on kitchen towels, and keep warm in a low oven until you

finish cooking up the batter.

4. To make the lime dipping sauce, combine the lime juice, soy sauce and brown sugar.

5. Serve the dipping sauce with the warm salmon cakes.

Freestyle SmartPoints for one cake: 0

Nutritional information for one cake: 44 calories, 0.9g fat, 0.1g fiber

Makes 6 servings

Ingredients
250 g ground chicken
1 egg white, lightly beaten
100 g mushrooms, chopped
1 onion, diced
1 stalk celery, chopped
1 large parsley, sprig
1/2 cup breadcrumbs
2 teaspoons soy sauce, salt reduced
3 whole wheat English muffins
1 tomato
3 lettuce leaves

How you make it:
1. Process the mushrooms, celery, onion, parsley, egg white and soy sauce in a food processor until smooth.
2. Mix this with the ground chicken and enough bread crumbs to make a soft, but manageable texture.
3. Divide the mix into 6 and then shape into balls.
4. On a baking tray lined with paper, press the balls down and place in a preheated oven.
5. Serve on a muffin half with the lettuce leaf and 2 slices of tomato.

Freestyle SmartPOINTS per serving: 1

Nutritional information per serving: 172 calories, 2.6g fat, 3.5g fiber

Makes 12 kebabs

Ingredients
2 chicken breasts
4 pieces bread
1/2 cup breadcrumbs
2 dried garlic
2 big onions
2 green chilies
1/2 teaspoon black pepper
salt (as required)
refined oil (for frying)

How you make it:
1. Put chicken, onions, garlic, chillies, black pepper powder and salt in the blender and run until mixture is totally smooth (add very little water if at all necessary).
2. Transfer the mixture to the bowl.
3. Add bread crumbs and the bread pieces (crush them thoroughly with wet hands); mix them well using your hands.
4. Heat the oil in a pan (fill almost 5 1/2 inches for frying).
5. Take out small scoops of mixture, make small balls and flatten them a little before putting in the oil.
6. Fry on medium heat on both sides until well done.

Freestyle Smartpoint for one kebab: 1

Nutritional information for one kebab: 95 calories, 2.8g fat, 0.9g fiber

Makes 10 servings

Ingredients
2 medium bananas, diced
2 medium apples, diced
2 cups grapes
2 cups sliced strawberries
1 (20 ounce) can pineapple tidbits, drained, juice reserved
1/4 cup pecans, chopped
1 lemon, juice of
1 (1 1/2 ounce) box sugar-free instant vanilla pudding mix or vegetarian sugar-free instant vanilla
pudding mix
1/2 cup water

How you make it:
1. Combine bananas, apples and lemon juice in a large mixing bowl.
2. Toss until evenly coated.
3. Add pineapple, strawberries, grapes and pecans.
4. In a small mixing bowl, combine pudding mix, water and pineapple juice with a wire whisk until smooth.
5. Add pudding mixture to fruit.
6. Mix gently until thoroughly coated.
7. Refrigerate until ready to serve.

Freestyle Smartpoints per serving: 1

Nutritional information per serving: 128 calories, 2.4g fat, 3.8g fiber

Makes 60 servings

Ingredients
1 lb ground beef
1/2 lb ground pork
1 teaspoon poultry seasoning or sage
1/2 cup previously cooked and mashed potatoes
2 garlic cloves, finely minced
1 small onion, finely diced
1/4 teaspoon salt
1/4 teaspoon pepper
3/4 cup water

How you make it:

1. Combine first 8 ingredients in large saucepan. Simmer.
2. Bring to a boil, then simmer for about 15 minutes, stirring to prevent sticking.
3. Remove from heat and add mashed potatoes. Mixture should be moist and thick. Cool completely.
4. Line muffin tins with tart shells. Spoon meat mixture to fill.
5. Bake at 400 degrees F until browned.
6. To reheat from freezer, put in oven or toaster oven for about 10 to 20 minutes at 350 degrees F.

Freestyle Smartpoints per serving: 1

Nutritional information per serving: 29 calories, 1.9g fat, 0.1g fiber

Makes 4 servings

Ingredients
1 1/2 lbs fresh pumpkin, peeled, seeded and cut into 1/2 inch cubes
2 garlic cloves, minced
1 tablespoon Herbes de Provence
1 tablespoon chili powder
1 teaspoon cinnamon
1 teaspoon cumin
1/2 tablespoon good quality balsamic vinegar
4 tablespoons good quality olive oil

How you make it:
1. Preheat the oven to 450°F.
2. Spray an oven proof baking dish with non-stick cooking spray (or you can butter the baking dish if you prefer).
3. In a bowl, mix the garlic, Herbes de Provence, chili powder, cinnamon, cumin, Balsamic vinegar and olive oil.
4. Add the pumpkin and toss well to coat.
5. Set pumpkin in the baking dish.
6. Place baking dish in the center of a pre-warmed oven 20-25 minutes; after 10 minutes coat the pumpkin with any additional coating left in the bowl.
7. Once roasted, pierce with toothpicks and serve.

Freestyle Smartpoints per serving: 3

Nutritional information per serving: 175 calories, 14.1g fat, 1.9g fiber

Tasty WW Fried Tortilla Chips

Makes 4 servings

Ingredients
8 corn tortillas
salad oil

How you make it:
1. Arrange 8 corn tortillas in a stack and cut into 6 equal wedges.
2. Pour about 1/2 inch salad oil in a deep 2 or 3-quart pan and set on medium-high to high heat.
3. When oil is hot enough to make a piece of tortilla sizzle, add tortilla pieces, a handful at a time,
and stir to separate.
4. Cook until crisp (1 to 1-1/2 minutes); lift from oil with slotted spoon and drain on paper towels.

Freestyle Smartpoints per serving: 1
Nutritional information per serving: 104 calories, 1.4g fat, 3.0g fiber

Delicious WW Graham Crackers

Makes 24 servings

Ingredients
1/2 cup shortening
3/4 cup packed brown sugar
1 teaspoon vanilla extract
2 cups whole-wheat flour
1 cup all-purpose flour
1 teaspoon baking powder
1/2 teaspoon baking soda
1/4 teaspoon salt
1/4 cup milk

How you make it:
1. In a medium bowl, cream together the shortening and brown sugar.
2. Stir in the vanilla.
3. Combine the whole wheat flour, all-purpose flour, baking powder, baking soda and salt, stir into the creamed mixture alternately with the milk.
4. Cover and chill dough until firm.
5. Preheat oven to 350 degrees F.
6. Grease cookie sheets.
7. On a lightly floured surface, roll the dough out to 0.125

inch thickness.

8. Cut into rectangles or circles.

9. Place 1/2 inch apart onto the prepared cookie sheets.

10. Bake for 10-12 minutes in the preheated oven, or until crisp.

11. Edges will be golden brown.

12. Remove from baking sheet to cool on wire racks.

Freestyle Smartpoints per serving: 1

Nutritional information per serving: 119 calories, 4.6g fat, 1.4g fiber

SERVES 1

Ingredients:

1/2 cup fat-free egg substitute

1/8 teaspoon salt

1/8 teaspoon black pepper

1 tsp canola oil

2 tbsp. shredded low-fat Swiss cheese

¼ cup frozen chopped asparagus, thawed

¼ cup frozen peas, thawed

¼ cup chopped red bell pepper

2 tbsp. chopped fresh chives or scallions

How you make it

1. Whisk together egg substitute, salt, and black pepper in medium bowl.

2. Heat oil in medium nonstick skillet over medium heat. Add egg mixture and cook, stirring gently, until underside is set, about 1 minute.

3. Sprinkle Swiss, asparagus, peas, and bell pepper over half of omelette. Fold unfilled half of omelette over to enclose filling. Cook until cheese is melted, about 2 minutes.

4. Slide omelette onto plate and sprinkle with chives.

PER SERVING (1 omelette): 181 Cal

6 g Total Fat, 1 g Sat Fat

0 g Trans Fat, 5 mg Chol

615 mg Sodium, 13 g Total Carb

4 g Fiber, 20 g Protein

206 mg Calcium

Freestyle SmartPoint value: 2

Ingredients

3/4 cup old fashioned oats

1 1/4 cups wheat flour

2 tablespoons granulated sugar

1/4 teaspoon baking soda

1 teaspoon baking powder

1/4 teaspoon salt

1/3 cup dried fruit (cranberries, currants, raisins, etc.) (optional)

2/3 cup buttermilk

1/4 cup light butter or 1/4 cup margarine

1 tablespoon half-and-half (optional)

2 teaspoons vanilla extract

1 tablespoon buttermilk (for brushing)

extra sugar (optional)

How you make it:

1. Preheat the oven to 450 degrees Fahrenheit.

2. Mix together the dry ingredients (oats, flour, sugar, baking soda, baking powder, salt).

3. Cut in the butter and combine using a fork until the mixture resembles bread crumbs.

4. Add the dried fruit to the dry mixture if desired.

5. In a separate bowl, mix together the wet ingredients

(half-and-half, buttermilk, vanilla).

6. Gradually add the wet mixture to the flour mixture and combine until a soft and sticky dough is formed.

7. Move the dough to a lightly floured surface and knead 2-3 times. Do not overwork the dough.

8. Roll the dough into a 6-8-inch circle and cut into 8 pie-shaped slices (or you can experiment with other dough shapes such as circles to maximize the number of servings).

9. Bake in the oven for about 15-18 minutes, or until a toothpick inserted in the middle comes out clean and the scones are golden-brown.

10. For a golden color and extra crunch, brush the top of the scones with buttermilk. Sprinkle some sugar on top and broil for a few minutes, turning and adjusting as necessary.

Servings: 8

Nutritional information for one serving:

1 Freestyle SmartPoints

Calories: 153

Total fat: 5.1 g

Cholesterol: 8.5 mg

Sodium: 214.3 mg

Total carbs: 23.1 g

Dietary fiber: 2.7 g

Ingredients
1 large pear
1 tablespoon whole half walnuts (or pecans)
2 tablespoons no-fat cream cheese
vegetable oil cooking spray
2 teaspoons honey
1/8 teaspoon nutmeg
1/8 teaspoon salt

How you make it:
1. Preheat the oven to 350 degrees F.
2. If you wish, peel the pear. Slice the pear in half lengthwise, and scoop out seeds to make a nice circle. Spray with cooking spray and set aside in a gratin dish sprayed with cooking spray, cut side up.
3. In a small bowl mix together 1 teaspoon honey, the cream cheese, nutmeg and salt. Fill each pear half cavity with half of the cheese mixture.
4. Place a half walnut or pecan on top of the cheese mixture, lightly pressing it down. Drizzle the pear halves with the remaining teaspoon of honey.
5. Roast the pear halves on the center grate of the oven for about 1 hour (or until soft). Test with a toothpick at about 45 minutes.

Servings: 2

Nutritional information for one serving:
Freestyle SmartPoints: 1
Calories: 156
Calories from fat: 68
Total fat: 7.6g
Cholesterol: 15mg
Sodium: 189mg
Total carbs: 22.8g
Dietary fiber: 3.5g
Protein: 2.1g

Ingredients

8 teaspoons jelly or jam or preserves (1/4 teaspoon for each cracker)

16 teaspoons creamy peanut butter (1/2 teaspoon for each cracker)

32 Ritz crackers or saltine crackers

How you Make it:

1. Smear the peanut butter, then the jelly or jam on the crackers.

2. Place the appetizers on a pretty tray and serve.

Servings: 32

Nutritional information for one serving:

Freestyle SmartPoints: 0

Calories: 32

Calories from fat: 15

Total fat: 1.7g

Cholesterol: 0mg

Total carbs: 3.8g

Fiber: 0.3g

Protein: 1g

Makes 12 servings

Ingredients
3 slices bacon, cooked, drained and crumbled
1 (15 ounce) can navy beans, drained
1/2 cup crumbled Blue cheese (2 ounces)
1 garlic clove, chopped
1/4 cup chopped onion
1 teaspoon chopped fresh thyme
1 tablespoon chopped fresh parsley
1/4 teaspoon salt
1/4 teaspoon fresh ground black pepper

How you make it:

1. Place the beans, garlic, onion, parsley, thyme, salt and pepper in a food processor or blender and
blend until smooth.
2. In a bowl, combine the bean mixture with the bacon and Blue cheese.
3. Serve with warm pita wedges or toasted baguette slices.

Freestyle Smartpoints per serving: 2

Nutritional information per serving: 97 calories, 4.4g fat, 3.8g fiber

Makes 32 sandwich triangles

Ingredients
1 large seedless cucumber
8 thin slices firm whole wheat bread, crusts removed
8 thin slices firm white bread, crusts removed
125 g unsalted butter, softened
1 teaspoon orange zest, grated
thin orange slices, to garnish
fresh mint sprigs, to garnish

How you make it
1. Peel the cucumber, cut in half lengthwise, and slice crosswise as thinly as possible.
2. In a small bowl, combine the orange zest with the butter, stirring until the ingredients are well
blended and the mixture is creamy.
3. Spread each slice of whole wheat bread with the butter mixture, arrange a few slices of cucumber
on each slice and top with the white bread.
4. Cut each sandwich into 4 triangles.
5. Serving suggestion: Arrange the sandwiches on a platter (alternating the brown and white sides of
the sandwiches) and garnish with orange slices and mint sprigs.

Freestyle Smartpoint for one sandwich triangle: 2
Nutritional information for one sandwich triangle: 63 calories, 3.7g fat, 0.7g fiber

A very simple and delicious recipe that's perfect for breakfast or as an appetizer or snack! Only two ingredients, but such a tasty result!

WW Sausage Swirls
Makes 28 swirls

Ingredients
1 lb bulk sausage
2 (8 ounce) cans crescent roll dough

How you make it:

1. Open the cans of dough and place on a cookie sheet (trying to keep in one piece), unrolling carefully, and pinch all the edges together.
2. Cut the sausage roll in half, and spread it thinly over both pieces of dough.
3. Roll up the dough lengthwise and place it in the refrigerator for about 30 minutes (or until firm).
4. Preheat the oven to 375 degrees F.
5. Cut the rolls into 1/2 to 1 inch pieces and place the swirls 1/2 inch apart on the cookie sheets.

6. Bake for about 20 minutes (until golden brown and the sausage is thoroughly cooked).

Freestyle Smartpoints for one swirl: 2
Nutritional information for one swirl: 87 calories, 4g fat, 0.6g fiber

WW Bruschetta with Roasted Garlic and Cherry Tomatoes
Makes 6 servings

Ingredients
1 loaf Italian bread, sliced
1 garlic clove
For the topping
2 cups cherry tomatoes, cut into quarters
1 large tomato, diced
1 roasted garlic clove, mashed
3 basil leaves, chopped
1 1/2 tablespoons carrots, finely minced
1 jalapeno, minced
1/4 cup red onion, minced
1/2 tablespoon caper, rinsed
1-2 tablespoon extra-virgin olive oil

How you make it
1. Toast the bread in the broiler or on the grill.
2. Rub with the raw garlic clove.
3. In a bowl, mix the topping ingredients together.
4. Serve the garlic rubbed bread with the topping on top.

Freestyle Smartpoints per serving: 0
Nutritional information per serving: 176 calories, 4.2g fat, 2.6g fiber

Makes 1 serving

Ingredients
1 whole honey graham cracker
1 tablespoon light whipped cream

How you make it:
1. Break the graham crackers in half.
2. On one half of the cracker, place a tablespoon of whipped cream and top with another cracker half; press lightly.
3. Place in the freezer until ready to be eaten.

Freestyle Smartpoints per serving: 1
Nutritional information per serving: 37 calories, 1.4g fat, 0.2g fiber

Makes 1 serving

Ingredients
2 eggs
1 tomato
4 basil leaves
salt and pepper

How you make it:

1. Beat the eggs slightly with fork, adding 2 minced basil leaves, pepper, and a 1/2 teaspoon water.
2. Heat the pan, spray with cooking spray and add the mixture.
3. Cook until the eggs get a creamy consistency, stirring and scraping from the bottom of the pan.
4. Slice and plate the tomato top with the scrambled eggs, garnish with basil and season with salt and pepper.
One serving is approximately 233 grams.

Freestyle smartpoints per serving: 2
Nutritional information per serving: 171 calories, 10.3g fat, 1.9g fiber

Makes 4 servings

Ingredients
1 1/2 lbs red potatoes (about 4 cups), quartered
2 cloves garlic, smashed
1 teaspoon dried rosemary
1 tablespoon butter
1/2 teaspoon kosher salt
1/4 teaspoon black pepper

How you make it:

1. Place the butter and garlic in an 8-inch square baking dish.
2. Microwave at medium-high (70%) for about 45 seconds (or until the butter melts).
3. Add the potatoes, rosemary, salt and black pepper, toss well.
4. Cover and microwave at high for about 15 minutes (or until the potatoes are tender).
One serving is approximately 175 grams.
Freestyle Smartpoints per serving: 1
Nutritional information per serving: 151 calories, 3.2g fat, 3.1g fiber

Makes 12 deviled eggs

Ingredients
6 hard-boiled eggs, cooled and shells removed
1-1 1/2 tablespoon mustard
3-4 tablespoons mayonnaise
1 teaspoon horseradish
1 teaspoon sweet pickle relish
1 dash salt and pepper, to taste
1 dash paprika (optional, to garnish)
6 green olives, sliced (optional, to garnish)

How you Make it:

1. Hard boil the eggs; once they have cooled, slice them in half and place the yolks in a medium bowl.
2. Using a fork, smash the yolks until no lumps remain.
3. Add the mustard, mayonnaise, horseradish and sweet pickle relish.
4. Mix well, adjusting the ingredients to taste.
5. Add salt and pepper to taste.
6. Spoon the mixture into the eggs (or, for a fancier presentation, spoon the mixture into pastry bag and pipe into the eggs).

7. Garnish with paprika and/or olive slices. Serve immediately or chill for later.

Freestyle Smartpoints per serving: 0
Nutritional information per serving: 54 calories, 3.9g fat, 0.1g fiber

Yummy Oven-Baked French Fries

Makes 8 servings

Ingredients

16 ounces frozen crinkle-cut French-fried potatoes

2 tablespoons grated Parmesan cheese

1/2 teaspoon paprika

salt (to taste)

black pepper (to taste)

How you make it:

1. Preheat the oven to 450 degrees F.

2. Combine the parmesan cheese, paprika, salt and pepper to taste.

3. Place the potatoes in a medium bowl coated with cooking spray.

4. Sprinkle the potatoes with the cheese mixture, tossing well.

5. Arrange the potatoes in a single layer on a baking sheet coated with cooking spray.

6. Bake at 450 degrees F for about 13 minutes (or until tender).

Freestyle SmartPoints per serving: 1

Nutritional information per serving: 89 calories, 3g fat, 1.1g fiber

Makes 6 servings

Ingredients
2 ripe bananas
1 tablespoon lemon juice

How you make it:

1. Cut the bananas into thin slices.
2. Coat the slices in lemon juice.
3. Place the banana slices on parchment paper and bake them in the oven at 200 degrees F, turning every half hour and watching out for burning.
4. Remove them when they are crispy; let them cool cool, and store them in an airtight container.

Freestyle Smartpoints per serving: 0
Nutritional information per serving: 36 calories, 0.1g fat, 1g fiber

Makes 12 servings

Ingredients
2 apples (peeled, cored and sliced into rings)
1/2 cup milk
2 eggs
1 cup flour
1 teaspoon baking powder
1/4 teaspoon cinnamon
2 quarts oil (for deep frying)

How you make it:

1. Mix together the dry ingredients.
2. In a separate bowl, beat the eggs, then stir in the milk.
3. Combine with the dry ingredients.
4 Heat the oil to 375 degrees F (190 degrees C) in a deep fryer or heavy bottomed deep pot or skillet.
5. Dip the apple slices in batter and fry, a few at a time, turning once, until they turn golden.
6. Drain the apple rings on paper towels, and serve sprinkled with confectioners' sugar, and/or maple syrup.
Freestyle Smartpoints per serving: 1
Nutritional information per serving: 68 calories, 1.3g fat, 0.9g fiber

Zero Point Cinnamon Munch

Makes 12 servings

Ingredients
4 cups Rice Chex or Corn Chex cereal
4 tablespoons butter or margarine
1/3 cup sugar
1 1/4 teaspoons cinnamon

How you make it:
1. Combine sugar and cinnamon; set aside.
2. Melt butter over low heat.
3. Add selected Chex cereal.
4. Heat until all pieces are coated.
5. Continue for 5 to 6 minutes.
6. Sprinkle half of mixture (cinnamon and sugar) over Chex cereal evenly.
7. Continue to sprinkle sugar mixture over Chex until all is covered.
8. Heat one minute longer.
9. Spread on paper towel to cool.
Freestyle Smartpoints per serving: 1
Nutritional information per serving: 93 calories, 3.9g fat, 0.3g fiber

All New Orange Sponge Cake
Makes 16 servings

Ingredients
1 cup sifted cake flour
5 egg yolks
5 egg whites
1 1/4 cups sifted powdered sugar
1 cup orange juice
1 tablespoon finely shredded orange rind
1 tablespoon honey
1/2 teaspoon cream of tartar
1/2 teaspoon almond extract
1 teaspoon vanilla

How you make it:

1. Combine cake flour and 1/2 cup of the sifted powdered sugar, and set aside.
2. In a small mixer bowl, beat the egg yolks with an electric mixer on high speed for about 6 minutes
(or until thick and lemon-colored).
3. Gradually add the remaining powdered sugar, beating constantly for about 4 minutes.
4. Stir in the orange peel.

5. Wash beaters thoroughly.
6. In a large mixer bowl, beat the egg whites, vanilla, and cream of tartar until soft peaks form.
7. Gently fold yolk mixture into whites.
8. Sift flour mixture over egg mixture, 1/3 at a time, and fold in gently.
9. Turn into ungreased 9 inch tube pan.
10. Bake in 325 degree oven for about 55 minutes (or until cake springs back when lightly touched).
11. Invert cake in the pan, cool thoroughly.
12. Remove from the pan.
13. With a long tined fork, poke holes on top of the cake at 1 inchintervals.
14. For syrup – combine orange juice and honey in a saucepan.
15. Simmer for 5 minutes.
16. Remove from heat, stir in almond extract.
17. Spoon syrup evenly over the cake (a small amount at a time), allowing the cake to absorb the syrup.
18. Chill, if desired.

Freestyle Smartpoints per serving: 1
Nutritional information per serving: 99 calories, 1.4g fat, 0.2g fiber

Makes 12 servings

Ingredients
4-6 slices bread (white or brown)
4 ounces grated cheddar cheese
2 ounces green pitted olives, finely chopped
6 extra olives, cut into half (to garnish)
1/2 teaspoon English mustard powder
2 tablespoons good quality mayonnaise
2 sun-dried tomatoes, drained and finely chopped
6 cherry tomatoes, cut in half
salt
pepper

How you make it:

1. Stamp 12 x 2" rounds out of the sliced bread – the spare bread can be kept for fresh breadcrumbs.
2. Preheat the oven to 230C/475F and line a baking tray with grease-proof paper.
3. Lay the bread rounds on the lined tray and bake for about 3 to 5 minutes or until a pale golden brown. Remove from the oven.
4. Mix the grated cheese, chopped olives, chopped sun-dried tomatoes, mustard powder and

mayonnaise together – season with salt and pepper to taste (remembering the olives are already quite salty).

5. Spread the mixture over the top of the pre-toasted bread rounds and bake in the preheated oven for about 5 to 8 minutes, or until the mixture has melted and is bubbling.

6. Take the mini rarebits out and place half a cherry tomato into the toppping of each round – put them back into the oven for about 1 to 2 minutes to soften the tomato, make sure they do not brown too much.

7. Take them out of the oven and finish off by placing half an olive in the middle of each cherry tomato as a final garnish.

8. Serve warm or at room temperature with cocktails, wine and other hors d'oeuvres.

9. The toasted bread rounds can be stored for up to a week in an airtight tin, and the cheese rarebit mixture can be made ahead and stored for up to 3 days in the fridge.

Freestyle Smartpoints per serving: 1
Nutritional information per serving: 81 calories, 5.1g fat, 0.6g fiber

Makes 8 servings

Ingredients
8 crackers
50 g cheddar cheese
1 small brown onion

How you make it:
1. Slice the cheese and onion.
2. Place a slice of onion on each cracker and top with a slice of cheese.

Freestyle Smartpoints per serving: 1
Nutritional information per serving: 43 calories, 2.8g fat, 0.2g fiber

Makes 5 dozen

Ingredients

1 lb confectioners' sugar

3 teaspoons butter or margarine, softened

2-3 teaspoons peppermint extract

1/2 teaspoon vanilla extract

1/4 cup evaporated milk

2 (12 ounce) cups semi-sweet chocolate chips

2 teaspoons shortening

How you make it:

1. In a bowl, combine first four ingredients.

2. Add milk and mix well.

3. Roll into 1-inch balls and place on a waxed paper-lined cookie sheet.

4. Chill for 20 minutes.

5. Flatten with a glass to 1/4".

6. Chill for 30 minutes.

7. In a double boiler or microwave-safe bowl, melt chocolate chips and shortening.

8. Dip patties and place on waxed paper to harden.

Freestyle Smartpoints per patty: 1

Nutritional information per patty: 88 calories, 3.8g fat, 0.6g fiber

WW Freestyle Weekly Menu Planner

Day /Time	Breakfast	Lunch	Dinner	Desserts
Monday				
Tuesday				
Wednesday				
Thursday				
Friday				
Saturday				
Sunday				

WW Freestyle Glossary List

Weight Watchers Freestyle Journal

This weight watchers Journal is easy to use and will help you immensely in achieving your weight loss Goals. Simply jot down the food that you eat and its point and then deduct it from your Daily Point balance. We have prepared a journal for you, where you can easily track your weekly Smart points allowance and Rollover Points.

Here is a sneak peak of how it looks

Today's Goal		Date	
Age	Height	Weight	

Food	Value	Balance
Smart Point Total:		
Rollover Point:		

Water ☐☐☐☐☐☐☐☐☐☐ Vitamins ☐☐☐☐☐☐☐☐☐

Protein ☐☐☐☐☐☐☐☐☐☐ Fruits/Veggies ☐☐☐☐☐☐☐☐

Exercise

Note

Visit this links below to get one Now

My Weight Watchers Freestyle Journal 2018>> Amazon link>> https://www.amazon.com/dp/1948191172

My Weight Watchers Flex Journal 2018 >> Amazon Link>>

https://www.amazon.com/dp/1948191180

My Weight Watchers Freestyle & Flex Instant Pot Recipes>> Amazon Link>>

https://www.amazon.com/dp/1948191199

Conclusion

- The best aspect of the weight watchers freestyle plan is there isn't any limit to the foods one can and cannot eat. So, when it comes to comparisons to other forms of weight loss diets, WW freestyle is easier to follow, as it also offers community support. It is an amazing plan for those people looking to lose weight without making drastic changes to their lifestyle.

- With up to four points daily roll overs, and more zero points food to save up on the allocated daily points, it is easier and more flexible than the older plans.

- The freestyle plan is great for vegetarians and sea food lovers with the added variety of fish (anchovies, arctic char, bluefish, branzino, butter fish, carp, catfish, cod, drum, eel, flounder, gefilte, grouper, haddock, halibut, herring, mackerel, perch, whitefish, pike, sardines, salmon, pompano, sea bass, smelt, tuna, tilefish, roe, sablefish, snapper, tilapia...)

- It would encourage creativity by encouraging one to make the most of the food available to them.

- The down side to this plan however is that while the previous plan was focused on weight loss, this new plan is concerned with healthy eating, and with a wider range of zero point food to complement, members could be basked in expending their whole points on others sources of foods with value points, and using the zero points foods as fillers.

- We have provided A weekly Menu Planner that you can print and use to jumpstart your weight loss goals. We wish you all the best, don't forget to drop us a review on amazon. Let's know what you think about this Diet Plan.

Made in the USA
San Bernardino, CA
28 January 2018